HORRIBLE SCIENCE
TEACHERS' RESOURCES

THE HUMAN BODY

Nick Arnold • Tony De Saulles
additional material David Tomlinson

AUTHOR
Nick Arnold

ILLUSTRATIONS
Tony De Saulles

ADDITIONAL MATERIAL
David Tomlinson

EDITOR
Wendy Tse

ASSISTANT EDITOR
Charlotte Ronalds

SERIES DESIGNER
Joy Monkhouse

DESIGNER
Erik Ivens
Micky Pledge

This book contains extracts from *Blood, Bones and Body Bits*; *Disgusting Digestion* and *The Body Owner's Handbook* in the Horrible Science series.
Text © 1996, 1998, 2002, Nick Arnold.
Illustrations © 1996, 1998, 2002, Tony De Saulles.
First published by Scholastic Children's Books.
Additional text © 2004, David Tomlinson.

Designed using Adobe InDesign

Published by Scholastic Ltd
Villiers House
Clarendon Avenue
Leamington Spa
Warwickshire
CV32 5PR

www.scholastic.co.uk

Printed by Bell & Bain Ltd, Glasgow

2 3 4 5 6 7 8 9   5 6 7 8 9 0 1 2 3

British Library Cataloguing-in-Publication Data
A catalogue record for this book is available from the British Library.

ISBN 0-439-97182-9
The right of David Tomlinson to be identified as the Author of additional text
of this Work has been asserted by him in accordance with the
Copyright, Designs and Patents Act 1988.

TEACHERS' NOTES

Horrible Science Teachers' Resources: The Human Body is inspired by the Horrible Science book *Blood, Bones and Body Bits*. Each photocopiable page takes a weird and wonderful excerpt from the original, as well as material from *Disgusting Digestion* and *The Body Owner's Handbook*, and expands on it to create a class-based teaching activity, fulfilling both National Curriculum and QCA objectives. The activities can be used individually or in a series as part of your scheme of work.

With an emphasis on research, experimentation and interpreting results, the activities will appeal to anyone even remotely curious about the Horrible world around us!

PART 1: Us

Page 11: Body types
Learning objective
The main stages of the human life cycle.
Adults have young and these grow into adults which in turn produce young.

Before starting this session ask your class to bring in photographs of themselves when they were younger. Compare these pictures to how the children look today, describing the changes. Introduce the concept that these changes will continue to happen throughout their lives, by showing pictures of yourself from babyhood up to the present day. Use photocopiable page 11 as a basis for class discussion before asking the children to cut out the figures and put them in sequence. As an extension you could encourage the children to predict how they might look in the future, making a class display of their work.

Page 12: Body facts
Learning objective
That science is about thinking creatively to explain how living things work.

Use the advert on photocopiable page 12 to focus your class on researching information about our bodies. Highlight any gruesome or surprising facts that they may discover. Set the children this task in research groups and encourage them to present their findings in the form of an advert. School libraries and the Internet will be useful information sources and this activity can also be extended as a homework.

Page 13: Class zoo
Learning objective
To make links between life processes in familiar animals.

Start this session by asking the children to look at pictures of animals in books or of any pets that they have at home. Encourage your class to look for similarities and differences between the animals and themselves. Use photocopiable page 13 to focus this research, asking the children to compile lists of differences and similarities as they go. Use their work as the basis of a 'class zoo', made up of drawings accompanied by a short piece of writing describing the animal, including a human specimen as your star exhibit.

Page 14: Look at me now!
Learning objective
The main stages of the human life cycle.
Adults have young and these grow into adults which in turn produce young.

Recap any work you have done about growth. Use photocopiable page 14 to focus your class on the early part of their lives, encouraging anecdotal memories. Talk about younger members of their family, highlighting the differences between 'them and us'. Focus on positive aspects of growing up (i.e. 'I don't fall over so much now') as well as social changes ('I am trusted to go to the shops on my own') and use these as a basis for a 'Growing Guide' written for younger children. As an extension you could present the growing guides to younger children, asking them how they see their older counterparts.

Page 15: Growth ratio
Learning objective
That the life processes common to humans and other animals includes growth and reproduction.
That human skeletons are internal and grow as humans grow.

Start this session by asking the children to describe the baby drawing on photocopiable page 15. Focus on Dr Grimgrave's notes regarding head:body ratio. Recap any numeracy work you may have done on measurement and ratio. Ask your class to work in pairs, measuring the length of their heads and comparing it to their overall height. Discover the present-day ratio between these two measurements and discuss it in terms of fractions. As an extension to the session, you could use this data to calculate a mean head:height ratio for the class.

Page 16: Reproduction
Learning objective
That life processes common in humans and other animals include reproduction.
That if living things did not reproduce they would eventually die out.

Recap any work you may have done about the children as babies, explaining that all humans start life in this way, dispelling the many myths and half-truths about 'where babies come from'! Use photocopiable page 16 to focus the children on the basic fact of females producing eggs and males producing sperm, and that when eggs and sperm meet a pregnancy can start. Explain that all mammals reproduce in this way and ask the children for examples. Use the cartoon to explain the journey a sperm makes in order to reach the egg, focusing on the word 'pregnancy', as many children will be familiar with this if they have younger siblings. Encourage the children to apply this knowledge to other mammals, finding out the differences and similarities in this process.

Page 17: What goes where?
Learning objective
That humans and some other animals have skeletons and muscles to support and protect their bodies and help them move.
Make and record observations about skeletons.

Use photocopiable page 17 to focus the class on the structure of the human body, asking the children to identify where they think the heart, lungs, brain, stomach, kidneys, liver and intestines 'live' inside the body. Discuss how they are supported and/or protected by the skeleton. Split your class into groups, asking each to research and draw one or two of these body parts, bringing them all together for a class presentation at the end of the session.

PART 2:
OUR HEALTH

Page 18: Get fit with Frankenstein!
Learning objective
The importance of exercise for good health.
We need exercise to stay healthy and maintain our muscles.

Start the session by asking the children to give examples of people they consider to be fit (i.e. football players, athletes etc). Ask them for their ideas on how these personalities stay fit. Focus on physical activities that the children participate in, as well as the benefits they get from activities they may not regard as exercise (i.e. running around the playground). Use photocopiable page 18 to draw together ideas of sensible exercise. Encourage your class to use examples from their own lives when designing a sensible exercise programme for Frankenstein's monster. As an extension you could ask the children to design a game or activity that incorporates different exercises and can be tried out in a games lesson.

Page 19: Healthy eating
Learning objective
The need for food for activity and growth, and about the importance of an adequate and varied diet. That an adequate and varied diet is needed to keep healthy.

Ask the children to name their favourite foods as well as some foods that they know are 'good' for them. Introduce the concept that these foods can be classified according to the basic food groups and that some foods are considered to be healthier for us than others. Use photocopiable page 19 to focus the children on classifying foods and encourage them to decide which foods they need more of than others.

Page 20: School dinners
Learning objective
The need for food for activity and growth, and about the importance of an adequate and varied diet. That an adequate and varied diet is needed to keep healthy.

Recap any previous work on food groups and use photocopiable page 20 to focus your class on the food they eat in school. Compare their school dinners to those on the activity sheet and encourage the children to decide what would make the perfect school dinner (i.e. one that is both tasty and balanced). Encourage your class to design a school dinner menu for a whole week and ask them to explain their decisions, relating them to the basic food groups. As an extension, invite the school cook to look at the menus and to show the children how he/she designs meals that are both nutritious and tasty.

Page 21: Vitamins
Learning objective
The need for food for activity and growth, and about the importance of an adequate and varied diet. That an adequate and varied diet is needed to keep healthy.

Ask your class to bring in a range of food packaging that shows the vitamins each product contains. Encourage a wide variety of foods, snacks and sweets. Ask the children to present their data and identify the different vitamins listed. Use photocopiable page 21 to help explain that a

deficiency in vitamins will cause us to become unhealthy and may have long-term effects on our health. Extend this activity to finding out what each of the major vitamins actually does for us.

Page 22: Freaky food files
Learning objective
The need for food for activity and growth, and about the importance of an adequate and varied diet. That an adequate and varied diet is needed to keep healthy.

Recap the basic food groups and use photocopiable page 22 to focus the children on fitting each group into a single sandwich. Ask the children to make a tasty sandwich that combines all the food groups. Discuss whether it is easy or difficult to combine all the food groups into a single meal. Ask the children to list all the different foods they ate the previous day, including any snacks and sweets. Classify these according to the food groups and award one point for each food. Tally these points and present them in the form of a bar chart. Use the information to see which food groups were the most and least popular. As an extension, ask the children to compile an individual chart for a week or correlate the entire class data bank to make a large-scale block graph for display.
Answers: 1 Yes, but it sounds horrible. **2** Yes, but it sounds equally horrible. **3** No, worse luck! **4** No, it lacks sugar and protein.

Page 23: Handling food
Learning objective
To present information about diet and health.

Start by asking the children why they are asked to wash their hands before eating. Introduce the concept that germs are invisible to the naked eye but can cause very serious health issues. Invite your class to take on the role of 'health inspectors' and to investigate the kitchen on photocopiable page 23. Ask the children to present their findings and to list their recommendations. Encourage your class to work in pairs and make a guide to food hygiene.
Answers: 1 Hair can carry germs even when it's clean, so it's a bad idea to comb it in the kitchen because germ-laden dandruff and old skin could fall into the food. **2** Hair not tied back or covered.
3 Blowing on food to cool it spreads germs from the mouth. **4** Dirty hands, fingernails and clothes.

Also not wearing overalls. Touching food will spread germs. **5** Flies go from dirt to food, transferring germs as they go. **6** Fridge door left open so the food isn't being kept cold. The cold should stop the germs from breeding so fast. **7** Raw meat and cooked meat must be stored separately to stop germs spreading from one to the other. **8** Rotten food overflowing from a bin will breed germs. **9** Cockroaches like dark and damp places and they spread germs. **10** Cats must be kept away from food and from the tabletop as their fur will harbour germs and mites.

Page 24: Smoking
Learning objective
The effects on the human body of tobacco.
That substances like tobacco can affect the way the body functions and that these effects can be harmful.

Start by showing the children an empty packet of cigarettes, focusing on the health warning on the side. Ask the children why the warning is there. Ask them to list the reasons that they may have heard why smoking is bad for our health and can lead to death. Discuss the reasons why people start smoking, using photocopiable page 24 to focus the children on the discrepancy between the cool image and reality of being addicted to nicotine. Present the warning adverts as a display.

Page 25: Mrs Ashtray
Learning objective
The effects on the human body of tobacco.
That substances like tobacco can affect the way the body functions and that these effects can be harmful.

Use photocopiable page 25 to show the children an example of a nicotine addict. Split your class into pairs and ask them to draw a full-size version of Mrs Ashtray, highlighting the many medical conditions that she suffers from. Alternatively, split the class into larger working groups, asking them to work in 3-D to make a different part of the character and put them all together to make a class model.

Page 26: Health warning!
Learning objective
The effects on the human body of tobacco.
That substances like tobacco can affect the way the body functions and that these effects can be harmful.

Explain that for many years governments from around the world have been encouraging people to give up cigarettes, using any pamphlets and posters you may have. Tell the children that their job is to discourage their peers from taking up smoking in the first place. Use photocopiable page 26 as a planning sheet for this health campaign. Encourage the children to incorporate the Mrs Ashtray model (see photocopiable page 25) as well as songs, poems or drama sketches into the presentation.

Pages 27 and 28: Alcohol 1 and Alcohol 2
Learning objective
The effects of alcohol on the human body.
That substances like alcohol can affect the way the body functions and that these effects can be harmful.

Start this session by asking the children what they know about alcohol. Include social and religious attitudes to alcohol as well as anecdotal stories. Use photocopiable page 27 to show the story of Frankenstein's monster, focusing on the gradual effect that alcohol has on him. Ask the children for examples of alcohol advertising that they have seen. Talk about non-alcoholic drinks. Encourage the children to design humorous health-focused adverts for these drinks and to present them in class.

PART 3:
PARTS OF THE BODY

Page 29: Eyes
Learning objective
Asking questions that can be investigated scientifically and deciding how to find answers.
That we see light sources because light from the source enters our eyes.

Start this session by encouraging the children to say what they can see from a window. Talk about times when it is more difficult to see, explaining that light bounces off an object and enters our eyes, enabling us to see the object. Use photocopiable page 29 to look more closely at the inside of a human eye, establishing that each eye sees a slightly different range of objects and that our brain puts these two images together to form a single 'view'. Compare the pictures produced at the close of the session.

Page 30: Eye tests!
Learning objective
Asking questions that can be investigated scientifically and deciding how to find answers. That we see light sources because light from the source enters our eyes.

Use the optical illusion at the top of photocopiable page 30 to show that there is more than one way of 'looking' at an object (the image could be a vase or two heads in profile). Use the activities on photocopiable page 30 to focus the children on using their eyes for a purpose, reminding them that their eyes work in a similar way to a camera, with light bouncing off an object and entering their eye through a hole in the pupil.

Answers: 1 b) There are 7 million light-sensitive cone cells inside each eyeball that can see red, green or blue. They work best in good light. We also have 124 million rod cells that work in poor light. They see in black and white. **2 b)** The pupils have to work together. **3 b)** There is a blind spot. This is where the optic nerve connects with the inside of the eyeball and makes things seem to disappear.

Page 31: Cheers ears!
Learning objective
Making systematic observations.
That vibrations from sound sources travel to the ear.

Start by playing the children some music and ask them what it is, how they recognise it and what body part they are using to hear it. Use photocopiable page 31 to look more closely at the inside of a human ear. Ask the children for examples of situations where hearing is very important, relating their experiences to the photocopiable. To demonstrate that we rely on hearing even more when we cannot see, ask for a volunteer to stand in the middle of the room with a blindfold on. Place another volunteer in one corner of the room and ask them to clap. Once the blindfold is removed, ask the child to identify where the sound came from by putting an X on a plan of the classroom, like an aural 'pin the tail on the donkey'. As an extension you could use masking tape to map out a maze, asking for four guides and a volunteer. Blindfold the volunteer and assign jobs to the guides (one will give a single clap to signal the volunteer to take a step to the right, another will give two claps for a step to the left etc).

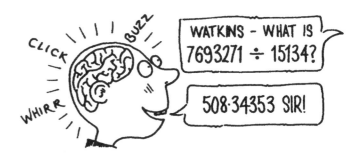

Page 32: The baffled brain
Learning objective
Making systematic observations.

Begin this session by asking your class to explain how to cross the road sensibly. Use this as an example of how the body makes quite complicated decisions, i.e. looking left and right, turning the head, assessing safety, walking across the road, and simultaneously assessing safety and distance using hearing and sight. Explain that although eyes can see and ears can hear, all this information is fed to the brain where it is evaluated. The brain works like a computer, using many different files for different information. Use photocopiable page 32 to focus the children on the simple concept that different parts of the brain are used for different jobs. Ask the children to write a check-list for the brain on how to cross the road, thinking about which parts of the brain are involved for each stage.

Answer: b) This allows the side of the brain that is answering the question to get on with the job without having to see at the same time.

Page 33: The skeleton
Learning objective
That humans and some other animals have skeletons and muscles to support and protect their bodies and help them move.
Make and record observations about skeletons.

Begin by asking the children to feel and describe their arms. Explain that the hardness around the elbow is a set of bones and joints and these are part of our skeleton. Use photocopiable page 33 to focus your class on the extent of the skeleton, asking them to research the names of bones and add them to the diagram. Use tape measures to measure their bones and compare them.

Page 34: Bones – the inside story!
Learning objective
That humans and many animals have skeletons and muscles to support and protect their bodies and help them move.
Make and record observations about skeletons.

Recap any previous skeleton work your class may have done, explaining that today you are looking inside the bones themselves. Use photocopiable page 34 as a class quiz.
Answers: 1 a) Yes, humans have tails. The coccyx is made up of three to five bones joined up at the end of the backbone. **2 c) 3 b)** Giraffe bones are longer! **4 c)** Lots of these extra bones join up as the baby grows. **5 b) 6 a) 7 b)**

Pages 35 and 36: The Wandering Bones! 1 and Wandering Bones! 2
Learning objective
Humans and many animals have skeletons and muscles to support and protect their bodies and help them move.
Make and record observations about skeletons.

Read the story of The Wandering Bones on photocopiable page 35, encouraging the children to solve the mystery using their knowledge about the skeleton. Ask your class to work in pairs to measure each other's skeletons. Use this information to produce 'Wanted' posters for a class display, complete with comparative measurements.
Answers: 1 Yes, females have wider pelvic bones. **2** Yes, as he grew older some of his bones joined together. **3** Yes, by the length of the thighbones. **4 5 6** No. **7** Yes, by looking at the build of the skeleton. **8** Yes, marks on the right arm bones showed traces of more developed muscles than on the left side.

After studying the bones the scientists were certain they had the right man. Final proof came when they found that an old photo of the outlaw's head perfectly matched the shape of his skull. And so, at long last, Elmer McCurdy's body was given a decent burial – nearly 66 years after he was killed!

Page 37: Joints
Learning objective
That humans and many animals have skeletons and muscles to support and protect their bodies and help them move.
Make and record observations about skeletons.

Ask a volunteer in class to walk into the room, close the door and sit on a chair. Ask the children to describe these movements, explaining how they think they happen. Use photocopiable page 37 to focus your class on the role different joints play in allowing our skeletons to move. Ask the children to draw action self-portraits, identifying the different types of joint at work. Ensure that your class understand that joints come in all shapes and sizes, right down to the tiniest movement of a little finger!

Page 38: Mighty muscles
Learning objective
That humans and some other animals have skeletons and muscles to support and protect their bodies and help them move.
That animals with skeletons have muscles attached to the bones.

Repeat the opening exercise from photocopiable page 37, this time focusing your class on the muscles at work in our bodies. Explain that we can feel our muscles below a layer of fat under the skin. Ask the children if they have ever pulled a muscle or suffered from cramp, and relate this to photocopiable page 38. Encourage your class to use the Internet and fitness guides in order to find out the name and location of as many muscles as they can. Challenge the children to discover the largest and smallest muscles in the body and to write a muscle user's guide. Ensure that the children understand they cannot even blink an eye without using muscles!

Page 39: The heart
Learning objective
That the heart acts like a pump to circulate blood. Muscles in the heart pump blood around the body.

Ask the children to locate their hearts, explaining how they know they have found the right location. Focus on the heartbeat, using photocopiable page 39 to explain what the heart is actually doing. Ask

the children to jump up and down ten times, placing their hands over their hearts. Encourage your class to share any differences they notice, especially with their breathing. Explain that the heart beats faster because the body requires more oxygen to be pumped around during and after exercise. Use the activity on photocopiable page 39 to show how the children can listen to a heart beat, identifying the link between heart and pulse.
Answer: b)

Page 40: Teeth
Learning objective
The functions and care of teeth.
The shape of a tooth makes it useful for a particular purpose.

Ask the children to bring an apple to class and start with a single bite. Encourage the children to draw the shape of that bite, comparing it to a partner's. Ask the children to take another bite, this time focusing on the different teeth we use for different jobs. The initial bite will be taken by the front teeth, first chews by the middle teeth and finally grinding is carried out by the back teeth before swallowing. Relate this experience to the information on photocopiable page 40, asking the children to count their teeth using mirrors and record their findings.
Answers: 1 b) 2 b) 3 a) or **b)** Younger children have four pre-molar teeth and adults have eight. **4 b)** or **c)** Younger children have eight molar teeth but adults often have 12.

Page 41: Tooth care
Learning objective
The functions and care of teeth.
Some foods can be damaging to our teeth.

Explain that our teeth need to be sharp and strong in order to do their jobs properly. Encourage your class to share their own tooth care practice, making a class list. Use photocopiable page 41 to focus your class on the results of not following a dental care routine. Encourage anecdotal evidence of visits to the dentist, using this to reinforce reasons for brushing regularly and avoiding too much sugar. Use toothpaste adverts to start the children designing their posters for a class display. As an extension, ask the children to produce a 'Good Teeth Guide'.

Page 42: Inside your tooth!
Learning objective
The functions and care of teeth.
The shape of a tooth makes it useful for a particular purpose.

Start by looking at the diagram of the inside of a tooth on photocopiable page 42. Relate this to any previous work, explaining that fillings are needed when decay occurs in order to repair the enamel. Use pictures of the animals named on photocopiable page 42 and discuss the food these animals eat, relating it to how humans use different teeth to bite, chew and grind food. Focus the children on the shape of the tooth relating to the job that it does, encouraging them to use this information to draw and label their own teeth, using mirrors for accuracy.

Page 43: Digestion
Learning objective
Ask questions that can be investigated scientifically and deciding how to find answers.

Ask the children where they think their dinner ends up and start a step-by-step journey plan. Use photocopiable page 43 to show the journey in full; focusing the children on the fact that each of them has up to eight metres of intestines coiled tightly inside them. Ask the children to measure eight metres of string, then to draw their favourite foods on photocopiable page 43. Split the class into small working groups and give each a strip of paper on which they should stick the food pictures. Bring the groups together and attach the strips end to end to make a full eight metres of digesting food for a class display.

I'VE GOT PINS AND NEEDLES IN MY STOMACH!

X-RAY VIEW

Pages 44 and 45: Digestion Drama 1 and Digestion Drama 2
Learning objective
Create, adapt and sustain different roles in drama. Discuss and evaluate their own and others' writing.

Read the story on photocopiables 44 and 45, recapping any previous digestion work. Explain to the children that they will be adapting this comic strip into a play, reminding them of any scripts they may have seen previously. Ask for volunteers to act the parts in the short scene on photocopiable page 45, encouraging the children to try out their own ideas and dialogue. Split your class into small working groups, asking them to write their own scripts, rehearse these scenes and present to the class. As an extension, use the scripts as the basis for an assembly.

Page 46: Staggering Stomach quiz
Learning objective
Ask questions that can be investigated scientifically and deciding how to find answers.

The quiz on photocopiable page 46 can be used either as a homework research opportunity or class quiz.
Answers: 1) True. **2)** True. They're caused by a throbbing blood vessel over the heart. When you're nervous you're more sensitive to this throbbing. It's nothing to do with real butterflies. **3)** True. Some people do. You just need to eat regular small meals instead of three big meals. **4)** False. **5)** True. The cold stops your stomach churning for up to half an hour. **6)** False **7)** True. The stomach wall contains 0.5 per cent hydrochloric acid. This is strong enough to dissolve a lump of food in a few hours.

Page 47: Your food and where it goes!
Learning objective
Ask questions that can be investigated scientifically and deciding how to find answers.

Ask the children to locate the mouth, throat, stomach, liver and intestines in their own body. Use an A3 copy of photocopiable page 47 to focus your class on where the food goes finally. Encourage them to use books and the Internet to find out what jobs the liver and pancreas do. Ask the children to add their research to their own A4 copies of the photocopiable sheet and to present their findings to the class.

Page 48: Putting it all together
Learning objective
The functions and care of teeth.
The need for food for activity and growth, and about the importance of an adequate and varied diet.
The heart acts as a pump to circulate the blood through vessels around the body, including through the lungs.
The effect of exercise and rest on pulse rate.
Humans and some other animals have skeletons and muscles to support and protect their bodies and to help them move.
The main stages of the human lifecycle.
The effects on the human body of tobacco, alcohol and other drugs, and how these relate to personal health.
The importance of exercise for good health.

Most children will be familiar with Frankenstein's monster from cartoons and comics, so challenge your class to work together to produce a model human with instructions. Use photocopiable page 48 to focus the children on planning the model. Get the children into groups and give each group responsibility for a different part of the body. Photocopiable page 47 is a useful starting point, to which the skeleton and vital organs can be added. Encourage the children to keep a 'Body Building Diary', noting their progress. Ideally this activity should be spread over three or four sessions. Encourage each group to present their part of the model, explaining how they made it and what its function is within the body. Put all the parts together and unveil the finished Frankenstein-esque product, plus instruction guide, to other classes in school.

NAME _____   DATE _____

BODY TYPES

- Human bodies change as they get older.

- What do you have in common with some of these bodies?

- Find the body type that is closest to your own.

- Cut out the bodies and put them in order, starting with the baby.

- Describe the changes that happen to these bodies in your own words.

_____

_____

_____

_____

_____

_____

Body facts

- The human body is amazing – take a look at this advert!

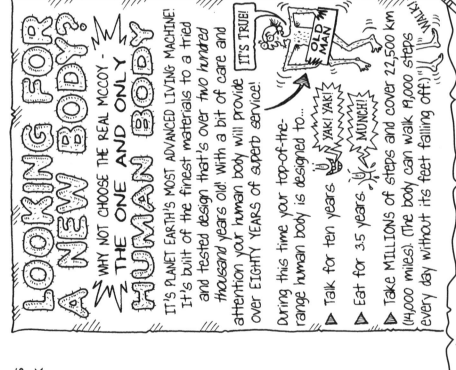

- Use the Internet and books to help you research some fascinating facts about your body.

- Design your own advert for the body. Write your facts using bullet points, like in the advert, and add your own illustrations.

NAME _____   DATE _____

Class zoo

- There are many differences between animals and humans – as well as some similarities.

- Humans can live for up to 120 years, although most stop working after 70 or 80 years.

- Take a look at these animals and find out how long they can live for.

- Choose three of these animals as the first members of your class zoo. What else can you find out about how their bodies work?

- Draw and write about the differences and similarities when they are compared to humans.

HE WAS **FELINE** FINE LAST NIGHT...

I GUESS IT WAS JUST MEANT **TABBY**

- Cats come a cropper after 15 years.

But body owners may be disappointed to learn that their human body won't last as long as some animal bodies...

- The oldest tortoise plodded on for 150 years.
- Sharks and lobsters seem to go on and on without showing signs of age until they're finished off by other animals.

AND I'LL FINISH OFF WITH THE SHARK-FIN SOUP

WHAT'S WRONG WITH LETTUCE?

YEAH!

Mind you, 99.9% of human body owners wouldn't swap their bodies for anything else. I mean, who'd want a body that lumbers around eating lettuce all day?

I FEEL OLD AND SICK

BUT YOU'RE ONLY 18 MONTHS OLD

YEAH, BUT I'M A SPARROW

SORRY, I FORGOT!

- Sparrows hop the twig after 18 months.

- Dormice are dead as doornails after five years.
- Swans sing their swan-songs after seven years.
- Dogs bow-wow out after ten years.

NAME _____   DATE _____

LOOK AT ME NOW!

- From the day you were born you have been growing!

- Babies and young children grow at an amazing rate.

- Draw yourself in the picture frames below. Include captions to show your progress.

0 months	3 months	6 months
caption		

1 year	5 years	Now!
caption		

- What do you like about growing older? What things can your body do now that it could not do when you were smaller?

- Write a guide for younger children telling them what to expect when they are your age.

NAME _____   DATE _____

GROWTH RATIO

- Our bodies develop from when we are a baby.

- Take a look at Dr Grimgrave's baby drawing.

In my honest opinion ALL newborn babies are plug-ugly. Here's a typical strange-looking case...

Often their heads are squashed as they are born. The bones in a baby's skull haven't yet fused together. (This is quite harmless and later puts itself right.)

Blotchy skin, wrinkles, and puffy red eyes.

one-quarter of a baby's body length is head and a baby's head is as wide as its shoulders.

- Measure your body parts and draw yourself in this picture frame.

- Compare your head length to the length of your body as a whole. What fraction of your body length is made up of just your head?

- Is this fraction different to the baby in Dr Grimgrave's drawing?

- Measure your shoulders and see if the ratio is the same.

NAME _____   DATE _____

REPRODUCTION

- Draw what the human baby looks like when he or she is born.

- Humans reproduce when they are adults. The mother produces an egg and the father produces sperm.

X-RAY VIEW OF EGG FACTORY (FEMALE)
EGG OVARY
TESTIS SPERM
X-RAY VIEW OF SPERM FACTORY (MALE)

- The sperm swims until it reaches the egg. Only one will make it.

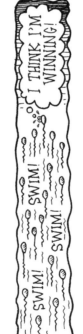

I THINK I'M WINNING!
SWIM! SWIM! SWIM!

SLURP!
MADE IT!
EGG

- Once the sperm and the egg meet up they start a nine-month growth process and we say that the mother is 'pregnant'.

- Other mammals reproduce in a similar way. Draw and label the babies that these animals produce and find out how long the mothers are pregnant for.

Cat   Dog   Elephant   Mouse   Rabbit

NAME _____   DATE _____

What goes where?

- We have 206 different bones in our bodies.

- We also have lots of different body parts with different jobs to do.

- Our skeletons protect these body parts.

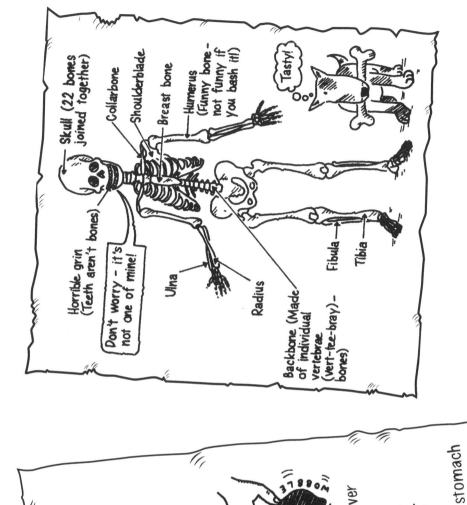

- Identify where the body parts go.

- Which bones protect which parts?

NAME _____ DATE _____

Get fit with Frankenstein!

- Dr Frankenstein's monster does not know how to exercise properly and has injured himself. Take a look at how this is affecting him.

- What will happen to his body as he gets older if he does not exercise at all?

_____
_____
_____
_____
_____

- What can he do to get fit sensibly?

_____
_____
_____
_____
_____
_____
_____

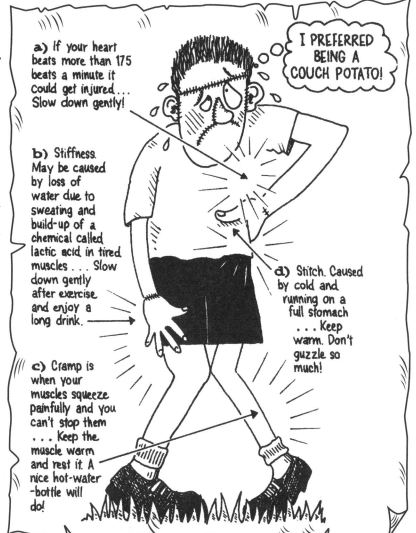

- Write a fitness guide for the monster to follow. Illustrate your guide with some really horrible diagrams of the monster doing your fitness workout!

- Now draw and label in the box what the new fit Frankenstein's monster could look like if he follows your guide to healthy and sensible exercising.

NAME _____   DATE _____

Healthy eating

- Our bodies need food from each of these groups, but we need some foods more than others!

1 Fibre helps your guts grip your food and keep it moving on its long trek to the toilet.

2 Proteins help your body build and repair its cells. Ten per cent of your body is made of this stuff.

3 Carbohydrates (car-bo-hi-drates) are found in starchy foods. Once they're digested they become sugars that your cells turn into energy.

4 Sickly sweet sugars are less vital, I'm sorry to say. These sugars provide your body with easy energy. Your lazy body feeds the sugar straight to the cells.

5 Fat is a useful store of energy and it helps build body cells – often in a wobbly layer around your tummy.

- Look at some foods that you know. Which groups do they belong to?

- Add them to this list – one of each has been done for you.

Fibre	Protein	Carbohydrate	Sugar	Fat
brown bread	eggs	rice	toffee	milk

NAME _____   DATE _____

School dinners

- The dinners on this menu look disgusting!

- We need to eat balanced meals which include sensible amounts from each food group.

- Design the perfect school dinner. Draw it on this plate and list the name of each food as well as the food group it comes from.

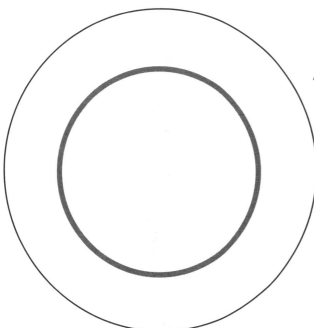

_____
_____
_____
_____
_____
_____
_____

- Design a healthy menu for your school for a whole week.

	Monday	Tuesday	Wednesday	Thursday	Friday
Main course					
Pudding					

NAME _____   DATE _____

VITAMINS

- We all need a range of vitamins to stay healthy. This chart tells us what happens if we don't have the vitamins we need.

- Look at your collection of food labels. Which vitamins do they contain?

Food	Vitamins

Vitamin	Found in:	Not enough causes:
A	Milk, butter, eggs, fish oil, liver.	Lots of illnesses and you can't even see in the dark.
B1 and 9 other B vits.	Yeast and wholemeal bread. Also found in milk, nuts and fresh vegetables.	Victim loses energy and can't get out of bed – sounds worse than a Monday morning.
C	Oranges and lemons. Fresh fruit and vegetables.	Loss of teeth, bleeding gums, dark spots on body. Bad breath. Yuck!
D	Oily fish, dairy products.	Bent bones and bandy legs. Bad news for footballers.
E	Wholewheat bread, brown rice, butter.	Scientists aren't quite sure about this one.
K	Green veg, liver	Blood doesn't clot properly – very messy!

- The vitamin chart tells us what happens if we don't have enough vitamins but what do they actually do for us? Do any of your favourite foods contain these vitamins?

Vitamin	What it does for us:
Vitamin A	
Vitamin B 1 and others	
Vitamin C	
Vitamin D	
Vitamin E	
Vitamin K	

NAME _____   DATE _____

Freaky food files

- Write down the ingredients for and make another sandwich that includes all the food groups. Would you want to have it for lunch?

- What did you eat yesterday?

_____

_____

_____

_____

- Look at your food list and decide which of the food groups you have eaten.

- Use this data for your block graph.

A sickening sandwich
Could you combine foods that contain fibre, proteins, carbohydrates, sugars and fat in ONE sandwich snack?

HAM AND JAM SANDWICH →

Here are some possibilities.
1 A ham and jam sandwich with a fizzy drink.
2 An egg and baked beans wholemeal-bread sandwich (yuck!) and a mug of hot chocolate.
3 A chip sandwich with white bread followed by treacle pudding washed down with loads of lemonade (burp!).
4 A healthy wholemeal lettuce sandwich followed by a sugar-free nut bar and glass of mineral water.

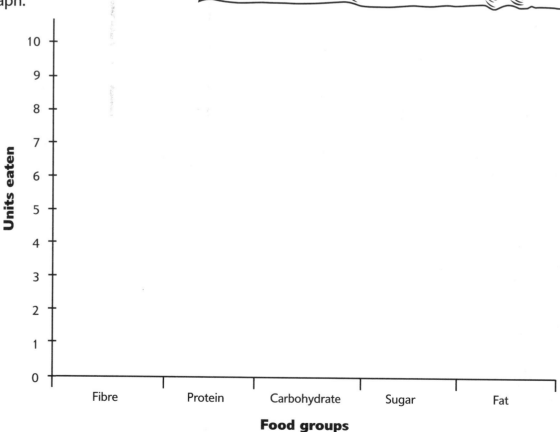

Units eaten

10
9
8
7
6
5
4
3
2
1
0

Fibre   Protein   Carbohydrate   Sugar   Fat

Food groups

Handling food

- Can you spot the germ danger signs in each picture?

- What recommendations would you make in your own Foul Food Report?

FOUL FOOD REPORT by M.I. Gutzache

At last, some real detective work! Something undercover. I'd heard that school kitchens were clean places that were inspected regularly by public health officers. But this one was different. It proved a real dirty business. Stomach churning, in fact, but I got the pictures in the end.

Germ danger sign	My recommendation

- Use your recommendations to write and illustrate a report called 'Clean food for a happy tummy'.

NAME _____   DATE _____

Smoking

- Take a look at this advert for cigarettes.

- What harmful effects can smoking have on your health? Make a list of them here.

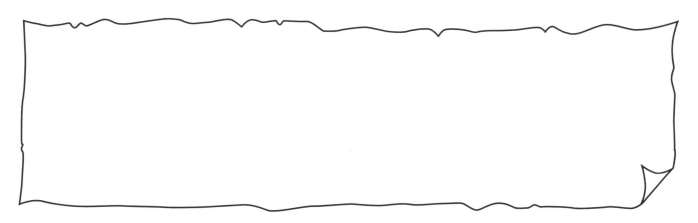

- Now use this information to create your own advert, complete with horrible details warning people about the dangers of smoking.

NAME _____   DATE _____

Mrs Ashtray

- Take a look at Mrs Ashtray's Patient Record.

PATIENT RECORD: STRICTLY CONFIDENTIAL

NAME: Mrs Ashtray

DIAGNOSIS: Mrs Ashtray suffers from smoking. The effects are obvious:

Wrinkled skin caused by tobacco poisons killing cells. Brown teeth (tobacco stains). Loss of teeth caused by gum disease.

PROGNOSIS: she is in danger of... Strokes due to blood clots forming in the brain and damaging the control systems for muscle movements. High blood pressure which can cause blindness. Breathlessness caused by lung damage. Diseases of her lungs and breathing passages. (Some smokers lose their diseased tongues.) Fat building up around the heart causing heart attacks (this is caused by nicotine). Diseases of her guts and bladder. Painful legs due to narrowing blood vessels and shortage of oxygen to muscles. Blood clots that may cause her arms and legs to rot. Some smokers end up having their arms and legs cut off in extreme cases.

ADVICE: Give up smoking AT ONCE!

DISEASED BODY PARTS

- Use this information to draw a picture or make a model of Mrs Ashtray.

- Include captions warning her about what may happen to different parts of her body if she does not give up.

NAME _____   DATE _____

Health warning!

Our presentation

Introduction:

Top ten facts:

Drama sketch ideas:

Ending song or poem:

ALCOHOL 1

Now, my dear readers, I would like to tell you the story of how alcohol affected the Monster at the Zombie's Halloween Party...

Midnight: Monster's first drink.

At this stage the Monster looks fairly normal...well, normal by his standards, ha ha!

12.30: Monster's third drink.

Alcohol dries the germ-killing spit and causes smelly breath.

Red face as alcohol widens blood vessels under the skin.

1 a.m.: Monster's fourth drink.

I ROAM GRAVEYARDS, I DIG UP BODIES, I SCARE VICARS... IT'S A REAL SCREAM...

YAWN!

Alcohol weakens hearing — making the Monster talk louder. The befuddled Monster thinks he's being funny when he's actually being boring.

2 a.m.: Monster's sixth drink.

I GESH THESH NO RESHT FOR THE WICK –HIC –KED...

Alcohol confuses the brain's speech systems.

Clumsy actions due to alcohol affecting the brain's movement controls.

Wider blood vessels mean more blood goes to the kidneys. The kidneys make more pee.

ER — S'CUSE ME!

Alcohol upsets the stomach causing vomiting.

The morning after the night before...

I WANT TO DIE!

YOU'LL HAVE TO COME ALIVE FIRST!

Alcohol dries out the body causing headache, tiredness and sickness. This stage is known as the hangover.

NAME _____   DATE _____

ALCOHOL 2

The morning after the night before...

I WANT TO DIE!

YOU'LL HAVE TO COME ALIVE FIRST!

Alcohol dries out the body causing headache, tiredness and sickness. This stage is known as the hangover.

NON-ALCOHOLIC ALTERNATIVES!

- Dr Frankenstein's monster could have avoided this!

- What else could he have had to drink instead of alcohol? Make a list.

- Sometimes alcohol is advertised in a way to make it look cool.

- Choose a non-alcoholic drink from your list and create an advert that looks exciting and also tells people the benefits of avoiding too much alcohol.

NAME _____   DATE _____

EYES

- Take a look at this advert to see how your eyes work.

- Now close your right eye and hold one finger in front of your left eye. Look at the view from your left. Draw what you see in box 1.

- Then close your left eye and look with your right. Keep the finger in the same position as before. Draw what you see in box 2.

- Open both eyes. What do you notice?

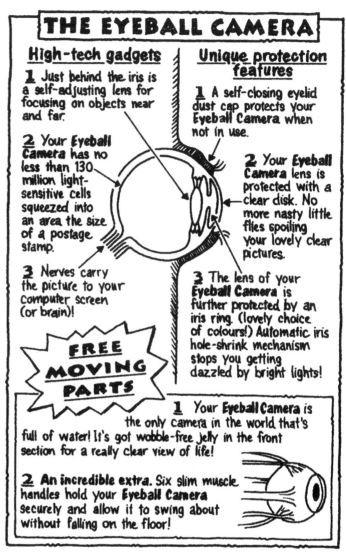

THE EYEBALL CAMERA

High-tech gadgets

1 Just behind the iris is a self-adjusting lens for focusing on objects near and far.

2 Your Eyeball Camera has no less than 130 million light-sensitive cells squeezed into an area the size of a postage stamp.

3 Nerves carry the picture to your computer screen (or brain)!

Unique protection features

1 A self-closing eyelid dust cap protects your Eyeball Camera when not in use.

2 Your Eyeball Camera lens is protected with a clear disk. No more nasty little flies spoiling your lovely clear pictures.

3 The lens of your Eyeball Camera is further protected by an iris ring. (lovely choice of colours!) Automatic iris hole-shrink mechanism stops you getting dazzled by bright lights!

FREE MOVING PARTS

1 Your Eyeball Camera is the only camera in the world that's full of water! It's got wobble-free jelly in the front section for a really clear view of life!

2 An incredible extra. Six slim muscle handles hold your Eyeball Camera securely and allow it to swing about without falling on the floor!

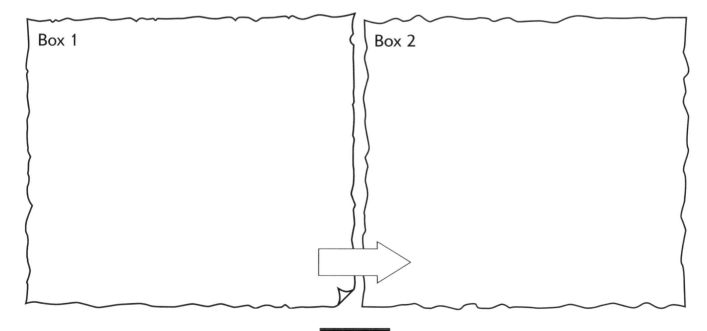

Box 1

Box 2

NAME _____   DATE _____

Eye tests!

- The brain can be baffled and our eyes are not always sure what they are seeing!

- Take a look at this picture. What do you see?

_____

- Try out these other tests too. Put a circle around the answers you agree with.

Test 1: Seeing in the dark

You will need a darkened room, a torch and a tomato. Shine the torch at the tomato and then away from it. What happens to the colour of the tomato as you shift the light away from it? Any idea why?

a) The tomato appears red both in the light and out of it. This is because the eye sees colour in the dark.

b) The tomato appears red in the light and grey out of it. This is because the eye can't see colours in the dark.

c) The tomato appears red in the light and blue out of it. This is because the dark confuses those little light-sensitive eyeball cells.

Test 2: Test your pupils

You will need a darkened room and a mirror with a light over it. Wait in the room until your eyes are used to the dark. Cover your left eye with one hand and switch on the light over the mirror. Your uncovered pupil suddenly goes smaller. What's happened to your other pupil?

a) It's still large.

b) It's also gone small.

c) It's got even bigger.

Test 3: The vanishing eyeball mystery

Hold this sheet close to your face and close your left eye. Focus your right eye on the left eyeball below. Now slowly move the sheet away from your face. Why does the right eyeball vanish?

a) The eye can't focus at a certain distance.

b) There's a gap in the light-sensitive cells.

c) The light-sensitive cells get tired and stop noticing things.

NAME _____   DATE _____

Cheers ears!

The ears work like a couple of satellite dishes linked up to a drum, linked up to a triangle and stick linked up to a microphone with a carpenter's level attached! Simple, isn't it?

1 Like satellite dishes, your ears pick up signals in the air and bounce them into the central hole. With your ears, the signals in question are sounds.

2 The eardrum's a bit like a real drum. It trembles when sounds hit it.

3 The trembling eardrum makes the tiny ear bones jangle just like a triangle hit by a stick.

4 The cochlea picks up the sounds and makes them into nerve signals that go to the brain. It's a bit like a microphone picking up sounds and sending them down a wire.

5 Like a carpenter's level, the semi-circular canals are full of liquid that sloshes around as your head moves. Sensors in the canals stop you losing your balance. This is good news for tight-rope walkers!

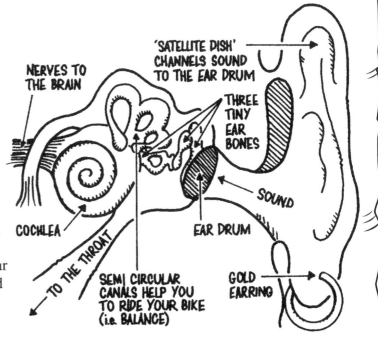

- NERVES TO THE BRAIN
- 'SATELLITE DISH' CHANNELS SOUND TO THE EAR DRUM
- THREE TINY EAR BONES
- SOUND
- COCHLEA
- TO THE THROAT
- EAR DRUM
- SEMI CIRCULAR CANALS HELP YOU TO RIDE YOUR BIKE (i.e. BALANCE)
- GOLD EARRING

- Now test them out for yourself. Stand in the middle of the room with a blindfold on. Ask a volunteer to stand anywhere in the room and ask him or her to clap.

  - Put an 'X' where you think the sound is coming from.

*

Me

NAME _____   DATE _____

THE BAFFLED BRAIN

Dare you find out for yourself ... how your friend's brain works?

Reassure your friend that this experiment does not involve any pain. And they won't need to have their head cut off either. Absolutely not! But you do need to remember some rather baffling information.
• The left side of your vision is linked to the right side of the brain and vice-versa.
• The left side of the cerebrum is the half that imagines where to find something.
• The right side deals with maths questions.

1 Write down five or more baffling maths questions.
2 And write another list of five or more baffling requests to give directions from one place to another, e.g. from home to school.
3 Don't tell your friend the aim of the experiment. Stand facing them about three paces away.
4 Ask your friend a maths question followed by a whereabouts question until you have completed both lists.
5 Watch their eye movements. What happens?

a) Their eyes roll upwards before they answer the whereabouts questions and go cross-eyed with the maths questions.
b) Their eyes go right for the maths questions and left for the whereabouts questions.
c) Their eyes go left for the maths questions and right for the whereabouts questions.

My maths questions	My directions questions

NAME _____   DATE _____

The skeleton

- Take a look at your skeleton.

- Which bones can you feel straight away?

- Are there any others that you can find?

- Name as many of them as you can and show where they go on the skeleton below.

_____

_____

_____

_____

_____

- Choose eight of your bones and measure them, adding these measurements to the skeleton.

Name of body part: Bones

Where found: Your bones form the skeleton that makes up about 25 per cent of your weight. Bones are made from a tough stringy substance called collagen (collar-gen), and strengthened with a mixture of hard materials.

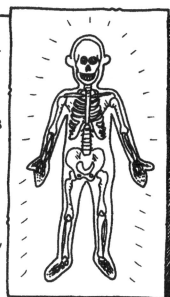

Useful things they do: They hold your body upright and give your muscles something to pull against.

Grisly details: If you took all the minerals out of your thigh bone you could tie what's left in a knot.

Amazing features: A broken bone repairs itself. As long as the broken ends are "set" or put back together – new bone grows over the break.

Bet you never knew!
Some people have more than 206 bones. People who spend most of their time riding horses often develop extra bones in their thighs. Some people have an extra pair of ribs and a few people even have extra fingers and toes!

NAME _____   DATE _____

Bones – the inside story!

Some bones are solid with an area of spongy bone on the inside, others are long and hollow and their empty centres are filled with the juicy jelly-like red marrow. Dogs love marrow because it's full of meaty goodness. So should you. Your marvellous marrow makes you 173 BILLION brand-new blood cells every day.

Look at bones through a microscope and you'll see they've all got little holes in them. These tiny tunnels carry blood vessels and nerves.

They're called Harversian canals (Have-er-shun) after their oddly named discoverer – Clopton Havers. It may seem odd to call these tiny tubes "canals" but it sounds better than "Clopton's bone-holes" at least.

Bone-groan test
How much do you really know about this interesting subject? Bone up on the answers to this ultra-fiendishly difficult test!

1 You will only find one of these bones in the human skeleton. Which one?
a) The tail bone
b) The elbow bone
c) The nose bone

2 If you wanted to hold up a heavy weight what would be the strongest thing to use?
a) A stone pillar
b) A concrete pillar
c) A leg bone

3 A giraffe has got seven bones in its neck. How many neck bones has a human got?
a) 3
b) 7
c) 12

4 How many bones does a baby have?
a) 206, just like a grown-up person.
b) 86
c) More than 350

5 Some Tibetan priests use the skull as a drinking cup. How much liquid do these creepy cups hold?
a) 500 ml
b) 1.5 litres
c) None – it trickles through the eye sockets.

6 What bone forms the sticking-out bit of your ankle?
a) The bottom of the tibia
b) The ankle bone
c) The top of the heel bone

7 What is a wormian bone?
a) A wiggley little bone in the little toe.
b) An extra bone sometimes found in a baby's skull.
c) A bone infested by worms.

The Wandering Bones! 1

It was 7 December 1976, Long Beach, California. The TV cameraman was in for a nasty shock. He was in a haunted house side-show filming a TV series. As he moved a gruesome dummy away from the rest of the film crew – its arm fell off! The arm was real. And there was a bone underneath!

The police were called but it soon became clear that this was no ordinary dummy – it had once been alive! The police discovered three fiendish facts. The body had been pickled in the deadly poison arsenic. It had been shot by an old-fashioned type of bullet dating from before 1914. In the body's mouth was a coin dated 1924.

The police then traced a series of former owners of the body. The former owners (who had all thought the body was a dummy) were colourful showmen who scraped a living exhibiting the gruesome specimen at funfairs. The oldest showman thought he could remember buying the body in Oklahoma. Then local history buffs dredged up a possible identity for the butchered body – Elmer McCurdy, cowboy and outlaw.

Elmer McCurdy's luck ran out at dawn on 7 October 1911. When the sheriff's men came for him he was drunk with stolen whisky and exhausted after a night spent hiding in a hayloft. A young lad was sent up to the hiding place.

"The boys want you to surrender, Mister!" he cried.

"I'll see them in hell first!" roared the outlaw.

McCurdy died with his boots on after slugging out a desperate gun battle until his six-gun was empty. After the outlaw's death an undertaker preserved the body and charged people to see it propped against his parlour wall!

Many people tried to buy the body but all offers were refused. Then the undertaker gave the body away to a nice man who said he was Elmer's long-lost brother.

Three months later the body appeared in a street-show in Texas.

But could the police bone experts prove that the body actually belonged to McCurdy? Here is a description of the outlaw dating from 1911. Which of the following features might you be able to check by examining the bones inside the body?

WANTED

FOR ROBBING TRAINS
ELMER McCURDY
(ALIAS FRANK CURTIS)
HAVE YOU SEEN THIS MAN?

1. Male
2. Age about 29-35
3. Height 170cm (67 inches)
4. Bearded
5. Thin nose
6. Deep set eyes
7. Slim build
8. Right-handed

NAME _____   DATE _____

The Wandering Bones! 2

WANTED!

Name:

Age:

Description:

Height:

Fingerprints:

NAME _____ DATE _____

Joints

- Our joints help us to move.

- Look for an example of each type of these joints in your body and write down where they are.

- Draw a picture of yourself scoring a goal or playing in the playground, labelling the joints you are using to move and play.

My joints!

Join up the Joints

Could you be a bone expert? If so, you'd need to know how to fit a skeleton together. The bones in a skeleton fit together to form joints and the trick is to assemble the joints correctly. But it's not easy – there are over 200 joints to join up!

Here are the main types of joints:

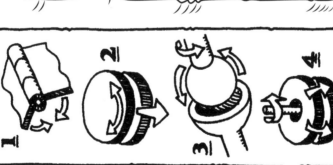

1 Hinge joint. Joints such as the knee work like door hinges, allowing the bones to move backwards and forwards. But they don't move so easily from side to side.

2 Gliding joint. The ankle bones can easily slide up and down and from side to side.

3 Ball and socket joint. As the name implies this is a ball and socket that allows arm and thigh bones to move in most directions.

4 Swivel joint. This joint allows the bone on top to move up and down and from side to side.

5 Saddle joint. The bone on top is like a jockey on a saddle. So it sways about and leans in all directions – without falling off!

NAME _____   DATE _____

MIGHTY MUSCLES

● We have muscles all over our body to help us make even the smallest movements.

● Take a look at this fact file.

Muscle labels

Name of body part: Muscles

Where found: Under the skin and surrounding various body bits.

Useful things they do: They're ALWAYS hard at work squeezing the food through your guts, pumping blood and so on.

Grisly details: Muscles can squeeze so strongly that they break your bones! But they have sensors to stop them squeezing that much!

Amazing features: Muscles are anchored to bones by tough tendons. A tendon won't go Twaang! unless you hang a 58-tonne weight from it!

_____

_____

_____

_____

_____

● Use the Internet and books to help you label as many muscles in the drawing as you can. Draw a line to the place these muscles can be found.

● Write your own muscle users' guide, explaining which muscles you need to use when riding a bike or even just watching TV!

_____

_____

_____

_____

_____

NAME _____   DATE _____

THE HEART

The horribly hard-working heart

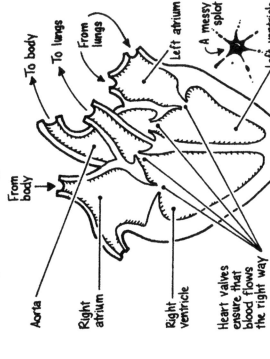

- To body
- To lungs
- From lungs
- Left atrium
- A messy splot
- Left ventricle
- Aorta
- From body
- Right atrium
- Right ventricle
- Heart valves ensure that blood flows the right way

Your heart is strong enough to pump blood around your whole body in one minute.

Its speed is controlled by the brain and influenced by your feelings – this is why your heart beats faster before a science test. But the heart itself is powered by a built-in pacemaker that triggers the heartbeat with tiny electric shocks. So it's got to keep going!

In just one day your heart pumps enough blood to fill a 10,000 litre (2,200 gallon) tanker.

In an average lifetime it beats 3,000,000,000 times. And pumps over 300 million litres of blood. That's enough to fill 5,500 large swimming pools!

And in all that time your heart doesn't stop once, not even when you're asleep.

Dare you find out for yourself ... how your heart beats?

- You will need yourself, a good pair of ears and a close friend. (If you don't want to get too close to your close friend you might want to get a plastic funnel too.) Just put your ear or funnel against your friend's heart. You should hear a sound that goes lup-dub, lup-dub, lup-dub, and so on. The "lup" should be louder and slightly longer than the "dub".

- Look at the heart diagram. Each of the four chambers pumps blood in the direction shown. The "lup" sound is the valves at the opening of the ventricles slamming shut. Then the ventricles squeeze the blood out and the "dub" sound you can hear is the closing of the heart valves to prevent blood squirting backwards.

- Your heart isn't the only part of your body that beats. You can feel the blood pulsing in places such as the side of your wrist, just under your thumb and on the sides of your neck.

What causes these pulses?
a) The arteries pumping blood forward.
b) The arteries bulging out as a surge of blood from the heart passes by.
c) A bulge in the veins caused by the blood stopping for a moment.

CAN YOU MAKE IT BEAT LOUDER PLEASE?

NAME _____   DATE _____

TEETH

Dare you find out for yourself ... what's inside your mouth?
Open wide! Here's where it all begins.
The gobbling, munching mouth – grinding up the goodies before they hit the guts.
Imagine what it's like to be a bit of food!

Tooth truths
The first thing you'll have to worry about are those gigantic spit-dribbling jaws. They're made from enamel and they're so tough you need a diamond to drill into them. Inside each tooth there are nerves and blood vessels just like any body part. Not all teeth are the same – there are different-shaped teeth for different jobs.

Premolars ____   Molars
Incisors ____   Bit of toffee (tut tut!)
Canines ____   3rd Molar (wisdom)
Incisors ____   Molars
Premolars ____

So how many teeth have you got? It depends on how old you are. You started off with 20 teeth that appeared when you were very young. As you get older these fall out and new teeth push through your gums. Here are some tooth totals – which is closest to your own number of teeth?

1 Incisors	**a)** 2	**b)** 8	**c)** 4
2 Canines	**a)** 2	**b)** 4	**c)** 8
3 Pre-molars	**a)** 4	**b)** 8	**c)** 12
4 Molars	**a)** 4	**b)** 8	**c)** 12

● The diagram above is of human teeth 'in profile'.

● Use a mirror to help you draw and label your teeth 'straight on'.

My teeth!

NAME _____   DATE _____

Tooth care

- If we don't look after our teeth, they soon get unhealthy.

- Apart from plaque and bad breath, what else happens to our teeth and gums if we do not look after them properly?

_____

_____

- What can we do to look after our teeth and gums to keep them healthy?

_____

_____

_____

- Design a poster to promote healthy teeth and gums at your school. Write some ideas for your slogan and logo below.

Slogan: Logo:

Details:

NAME _____ DATE _____

INSIDE YOUR TOOTH!

- We use differently shaped teeth for different jobs. Animals have developed to use teeth that suit their diet.

- Take a look at the teeth found in tigers, sharks, elephants, cows, cats and rats.

- Find out the link between the shape of their teeth and the types of food each eats.

- This should help you decide which teeth do which job in your own mouth!

- Draw your teeth and label the job that each of them does, using their scientific names if you have found them. Use the Internet and books to help you.

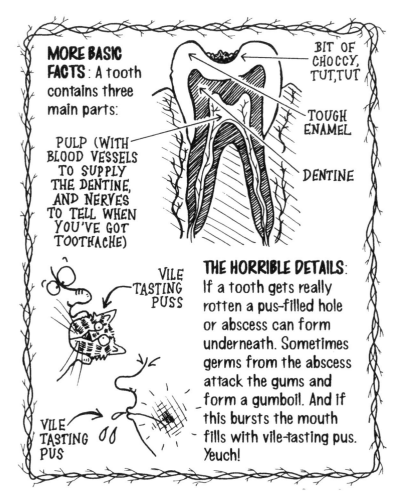

MORE BASIC FACTS: A tooth contains three main parts:

PULP (WITH BLOOD VESSELS TO SUPPLY THE DENTINE, AND NERVES TO TELL WHEN YOU'VE GOT TOOTHACHE)

BIT OF CHOCCY, TUT,TUT

TOUGH ENAMEL

DENTINE

VILE TASTING PUSS

VILE TASTING PUS

THE HORRIBLE DETAILS: If a tooth gets really rotten a pus-filled hole or abscess can form underneath. Sometimes germs from the abscess attack the gums and form a gumboil. And if this bursts the mouth fills with vile-tasting pus. Yeuch!

NAME _____   DATE _____

Digestion

THE GRUESOME GUTS

Guts are gruesome. Gobsmacking, grossly, stomach-churningly sickening. In fact – if you thought too much about where your food went you wouldn't feel like eating it! But if there's one thing even more gruesome than guts, it's the scientists who find guts fascinating. Oh yes, and then there's the smelly stuff that pours out the other end. Yuck!

- Draw your favourite foods below and cut them out.

- Add them to your class model.

- Work out how many metres of intestines there are in your classroom right at this moment: _____m.

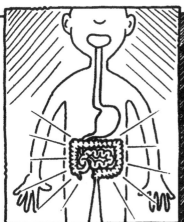

Name of body part: Guts

Where found: Mostly under the chest area in the lower part of the body. (See below.)

Useful things they do: Absorb your food once it has been digested.

Grisly details: The guts form a continuous tube up to 8m (8.7 yards) long. That's longer than a huge slithery snake!

Amazing features: Your guts are held in place by the mesentery (mes-en-terry). This stops the guts slopping about and tying themselves in knots!

Digestion Drama 1

A gruesome guts tour

Here's a gruesomely thrilling alternative to the usual boring tourist trip. Just imagine being shrunk down to the size of a pinhead and boarding a coach the size of a pea. Then imagine going on a guided tour of someone else's guts! And guess what? Your dinner's thrown in! That's if you feel like eating any . . . .

The Horrible Holiday Company proudly present...

THE GRUESOME GUTS GETAWAY!

EMBARK ON THE TRIP OF A LUNCHTIME.

THE SMALL PRINT

1. If you get digested and turned into a chemical soup it's not our fault – OK?

2. There will be **no** toilet stops until the end of the tour.

1.00 pm Enter the mouth. Fasten your safety belts and close the windows securely. It's wet outside and we're about to dive down the gullet waterfall. Splosh!

1.01 pm Amazing 9 to 13-second free-fall as we're squeezed 25cm (10 inches) down the gullet!

1.02–6 pm Five hour stopover in the stomach. Plenty of time to admire the slimy stomach walls with their 35 million digestive juice-producing pits.

▲ Enjoy the beautiful sunset effect as a red hot pepper makes the stomach glow.

► Listen to the mighty roar of the rumbling stomach as trapped gases squelch around amongst the food.

▷ Experience the gut-churning thrill of the stomach big dipper as it churns and churns again every 20 seconds. (If you feel a bit queasy, sick-bags are provided.)

NAME _____   DATE _____

Digestion Drama 2

Scene 1: In the mouth

Jack: (Looking excited) Blimey, Nabila, the holiday of a lifetime! I've always wondered what it would be like to go inside one of these!

Nabila: Yeah! Better than going to Blackpool again! Look at the size of those teeth...

Jack: (Pointing) There's a bit of fish finger stuck over there! Whoever owns this mouth needs to get their toothbrush out a bit more often!

Mysterious voice: Fasten your seatbelts, leaving Mouth for first leg of journey. Departing in 3-2-1...

(Nabila and Jack disappear)

Nabila: WAAAAAHHHHH!!!!

Jack: How did I get conned into this?!!!!

6.00 pm A sudden lurch takes us from the stomach into the intestine. Then what better than a relaxing 6m (65 yards) cruise down the scenic small intestine? (Speed 2.5cm (1 inch) per minute)

▶ Feel the lovely smooth gliding motion as we're squeezed along. The slimy gut walls help to stop the guts from digesting themselves.

▶ Marvel at the velvety insides of the intestines made up of five million tiny projections called villi.

▶ Gasp as we are covered in enzyme-rich digestive juices squirting down from the pancreas and liver.

▶ Wonder as the food chemicals are sucked into the villi.

▶ Puzzle over the mystery of the appendix. Everyone's got one of these finger-like things sticking out of their intestines. But no-one knows what it's for!

10.00 pm Spend the night in the comfortable and spacious large intestine. Here the surroundings are peaceful, lie back and listen for the relaxing gurgling of the water as it's taken out of the remains of the food and back into the body.

7.30 am (Give or take a few hours) Put on your life jacket and parachute. It's time for splash down in the toilet!

- What did you think of the journey?

- Use this story as the basis of a play you can perform to teach people all about digestion.

- Give your characters dialogue, feelings and directions.

- Set it out in separate scenes. You can use this example to start you off if you are stuck.

- The scriptwriter has called the characters 'Jack' and 'Nabila' but you can make up your own names.

NAME _____   DATE _____

Staggering Stomach quiz

How well do you know your own stomach?

1 The word stomach comes from the Greek word for "throat". TRUE/FALSE
2 Butterflies in your stomach aren't anything to do with the stomach. TRUE/FALSE

3 It's possible to live without a stomach. TRUE/FALSE
4 It's possible to eat and eat until your stomach bursts. TRUE/FALSE

5 When you eat ice cream the cold freezes your stomach. TRUE/FALSE
6 Your stomach stops moving when you're asleep. TRUE/FALSE
7 Your stomach produces an acid strong enough to dissolve a lump of bone. TRUE/FALSE

● Research some other true and false questions about the human body and try them on your friends or in a class quiz.

My quiz questions:

Your food and where it goes!

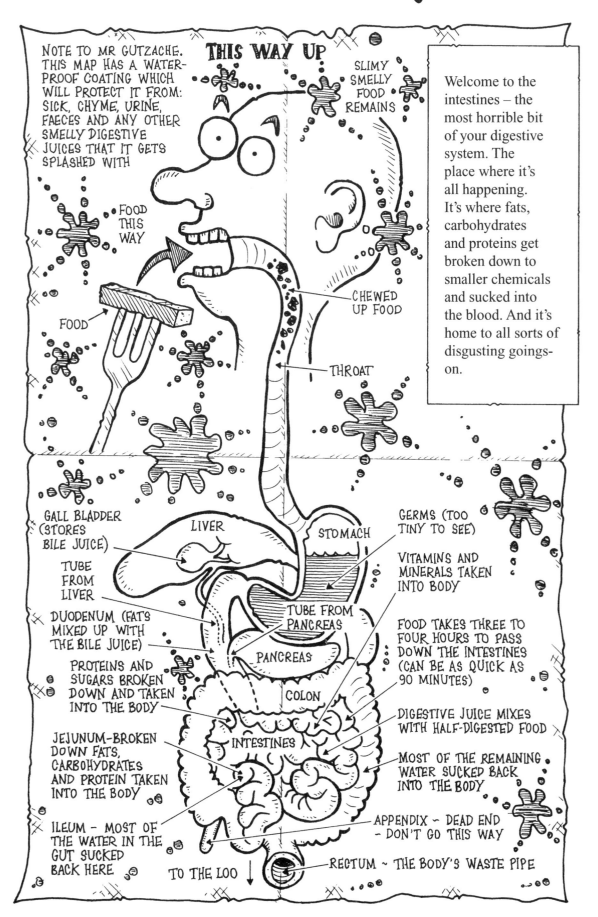

NAME _____   DATE _____

Putting it all together

Skeleton

Muscles

Teeth

The heart

Lungs

- Unfortunately our bodies are a bit more complicated than in this advert!

- Imagine that you are making a kit so that people can build a body, just like Dr Frankenstein.

- You will need to include these body parts ... and much more!

- Add your own ideas to this checklist.

- Use your science knowledge to make a model human and write a Body Kit guide.

How horribly charming to meet you!